Recycling Fun

Written by Lorraine Horsley

Mummy Pig

Peppa Pig

George

car

Daddy Pig

6

truck

Mr Bull

newspapers

bottles

cans

Miss Rabbit

7

Mr Bull is
collecting rubbish.

Mr Bull puts the rubbish
in the back of his truck.

11

Peppa, George and
Mummy Pig are
collecting rubbish, too.

They collect bottles,
cans and newspapers.

"We can recycle much of this rubbish," says Mummy Pig.

They put the rubbish
in the car.

Mummy Pig has
all the bottles.

Peppa has all the cans.

George has all the
newspapers.

17

Miss Rabbit is
recycling rubbish, too.
She is recycling cars.

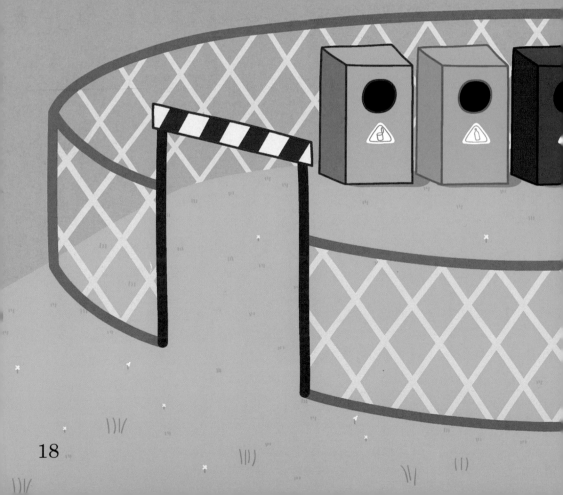

Daddy Pig recycles
the bottles.

21

Mummy Pig and Peppa
recycle the cans.

"I like this!" Peppa says.

George recycles the
newspapers.

Oh no! Miss Rabbit is recycling Daddy Pig's car!

"Stop!" says Daddy Pig. "Stop! That is not recycling! That is our car!"

27

"Oh," says Miss Rabbit.
"I like recycling too much!"

"Our car is not rubbish,"
says Daddy Pig.

"No," says Peppa.
"We like our car!"

How much do you remember about Peppa Pig: Recycling Fun? Answer these questions and find out!

- **Where does Mr Bull put the rubbish?**

- **What does Mummy Pig have in the car?**

- **Who recycles the newspapers?**

- **What does Miss Rabbit try to do with Daddy Pig's car?**

Look at the pictures from the story and say the order they should go in.

A

B

C

D

Read it yourself with Ladybird

Tick the books you've read!

Level 1

- The Enormous Turnip ☐
- Fairy Friends ☐
- Goldilocks and the Three Bears ☐
- Little Red Hen ☐
- The Magic Porridge Pot ☐
- Little Creatures ☐
- Recycling Fun! ☐
- The Princess and the Pea ☐
- Cinderella ☐
- Rex the Big Dinosaur ☐
- The Tale of Peter Rabbit ☐
- The Three Billy Goats Gruff ☐
- Why Giraffe has a Long Neck ☐
- Go to the Zoo ☐
- The Ugly Duckling ☐
- The Emperor's New Clothes ☐

Level 2

For beginner readers who can read short, simple sentences with help.

- Beauty and the Beast ☐
- Chicken Licken ☐
- Little Red Riding Hood ☐
- Nature Trail ☐
- Sports Day ☐
- Pirate School ☐
- Rumpelstiltskin ☐
- Sleeping Beauty ☐
- The Gingerbread Man ☐
- Sly Fox and Red Hen ☐
- The Tale of Jemima Puddle-Duck ☐
- The Three Little Pigs ☐
- Why Lion Roarrrs! ☐
- The Big Race ☐
- Town Mouse and Country Mouse ☐
- Dom's Dragon ☐

Available on the App Store

The Read it yourself with Ladybird app is now available for iPad, iPhone and iPod touch

App also available on Android devices

Level 1 is ideal for children who have received some initial reading instruction. Each story is told very simply, using a small number of frequently repeated words.

Special features:

Mummy Pig

truck

Mr Bull

Peppa Pig

George

car

newspapers

bottles

cans

Daddy Pig

Miss Rabbit

6

7

Opening pages introduce key story words

Large, clear type

Mr Bull is collecting rubbish.

Careful match between story and pictures

8

9

Educational Consultant: Geraldine Taylor
Book Banding Consultant: Kate Ruttle

A catalogue record for this book is available from the British Library

Published by Ladybird Books Ltd
80 Strand, London, WC2R ORL
A Penguin Company

001

Published by LADYBIRD BOOKS LTD MMXIII
Ladybird, Read It Yourself and the Ladybird Logo are registered or
unregistered trademarks of Ladybird Books Limited.

This book is based on the
TV Series 'Peppa Pig'
'Peppa Pig' is created by
Neville Astley and Mark Baker
Peppa Pig © Astley Baker Davies/
Entertainment One UK Limited 2003.

www.peppapig.com

ISBN: 978-0-72327-284-7

Printed in China